Are We There Yet?

By Janice Behrens

ISBN: 978-1-338-88859-1

Editor: Liza Charlesworth
Art Director: Tannaz Fassihi; Designer: Tanya Chernyak
Photos ©: 2: Rune Hellestad/Getty Images; 5: Sami Sarkis Travel/Alamy Stock Photo; 6: HBpictures/Adobe Stock; 7: Orbon Alija/Getty Images; 8: FangXiaNuo/Getty Images. All other photos © Shutterstock.com.

Printed in Jiaxing, China. First printing, January 2023.

SCHOLASTIC INC.

We read in the car.
Are we there yet?

We sing in the car.
Are we there yet?

We eat in the car.
Are we there yet?

We draw in the car.
Are we there yet?

We laugh in the car.
Are we there yet?

We sleep in the car.
Are we there yet?

Yes!